# And Pretend

By
Pamela Conn Beall and Susan Hagan Nipp

Illustrated by
Nancy Spence Klein

PSS!
PRICE STERN SLOAN

# PREFACE

Children love to pretend. Whether it's playing dress up, flying like an airplane, or galloping like a horse, imaginations soar when a child "becomes" the object of his pretending. This freedom of creativity contributes to emotional and intellectual development as the child expresses himself and continually makes decisions while pretending.

*Wee Sing and Pretend* expands the realm of pretend through the medium of music. A variety of tempos, dynamics, instrumentation, and sound effects create many different moods that encourage creative expression. Musical selections range from traditional songs such as "Row, Row, Row Your Boat" to original songs about dinosaurs. Classical favorites like "Carnival of the Animals," "Flight of the Bumblebee," and the "William Tell Overture" add another dimension to the pretending. We have included a wide variety of subjects familiar to children from animals to clowns to race cars.

Beyond the joy of pretending, children will become familiar with classical music, learn lyrics to new songs, experiment with different types of movement, and creatively determine how to enact each pretend.

We have had fun pretending while writing this book. In addition, we have found it to be a great source of exercise. We hope you'll join your children in the world of pretend and find great joy as you watch their imaginations take flight.

*Pam Beall*
*Susan Nipp*

# Animals

### LION

The lion is the King of Beasts,
He roams across the land,
With head held high, he gives a roar,
He's awesome and he's grand.

### WILD HORSES

Up and down and all around,
The wild horses race,
With dashing hooves and flying manes,
They love this game of chase.

### TURTLE

Although you think the turtle's slow,
He's looking at the scenery,
And sometimes he will slow down more
To stop and eat the greenery.

## ELEPHANT

The huge, enormous elephant
Moves slowly in the sun,
He dunks his trunk to drink from lakes
And rolls in mud for fun.

## KANGAROO

The Australian kangaroo is happy
Hopping through the day,
He hops, then stops to eat and rest,
Then travels on his way.

## FISH

Shimmering, glimmering, under the sea,
The fish swim quietly,
With flickering fins and swishing tails
And mouths that move silently.

## BIRDS

Flitting and flying, soaring and gliding,
Birds are everywhere.
They zip and they zoom, they dart and they dive,
Beautiful birds in the air.

*Susan Nipp*

(Saint-Saëns: *Carnival of the Animals*—1886)

7

# Dinosaurs

*I'm a huge brontosaurus dinosaur, stomping around on the ground!*

## BRONTOSAURUS

*Nancy Klein*                                    *Nancy Klein*

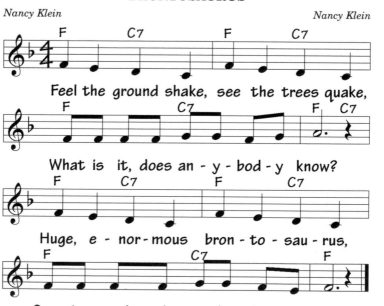

Feel the ground shake, see the trees quake,

What is it, does an - y - bod - y know?

Huge, e - nor - mous bron - to - sau - rus,

Caus-ing earth-quakes ev - 'ry-where he goes.

8

*I can soar high in the sky. I'm a big flying reptile, a pteranodon!*

## PTERANODON

*Nancy Klein*                                                    *Nancy Klein*

The great, wide pter - an - o - don soar - ing so high,

He'd glide with the wind and then dive from the

sky, He'd scoop up a fish as he skimmed o'er the

sea, This great fly - ing rep - tile was free as could be.

*I'm a dinosaur with long legs and I can run very fast. I'm an ornithomimus!*

### ORNITHOMIMUS
*(Bird Imitator)*

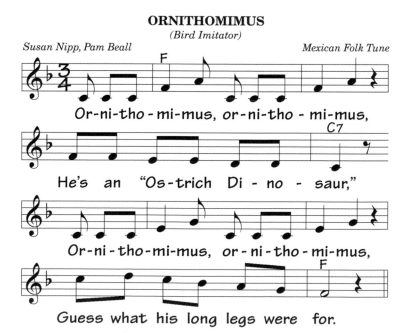

Or-ni-tho-mi-mus, or-ni-tho-mi-mus,

He's an "Os-trich Di-no-saur,"

Or-ni-tho-mi-mus, or-ni-tho-mi-mus,

Guess what his long legs were for.

10

(Chorus/Descant)

Run-ning, run-ning, run-ning, run-ning,

C7

Run-ning, run-ning, run-ning, run-ning,

Run-ning, run-ning, run-ning, run-ning,

F

That's what his long legs were for.

11

## MIKEY THE MONKEY

Susan Nipp                                                    Susan Nipp

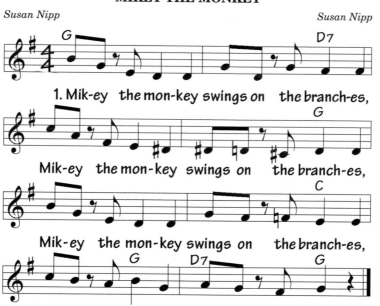

1. Mik-ey the mon-key swings on the branch-es,
Mik-ey the mon-key swings on the branch-es,
Mik-ey the mon-key swings on the branch-es,
Mik-ey the mon-key jumps to the ground.

2. Mikey the monkey peels a banana...
Mikey the monkey eats it all gone.

3. Mikey the monkey scratches his fleas...
Mikey the monkey shakes them all off.

4. Mikey the monkey makes funny faces...
Mikey the monkey scampers away.

# THE LITTLE CATERPILLAR

*Pam Beall*                    *Pam Beall*

1. The lit - tle cat - er - pil - lar inched his

way a-cross the branch, Nib-bling leaves a-long the

way, He looked up in the sky and saw a

pret - ty but - ter - fly, And he

won - dered if he'd fly some day.

Chorus

But - ter - fly, but - ter - fly, how you

fly so free, But - ter - fly, but - ter -

fly, wish that I could be A - ble to

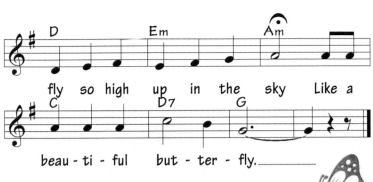

fly so high up in the sky Like a

beau - ti - ful but - ter - fly._____

2. The little caterpillar formed a cozy little shell,
   Then curled up with a sleepy sigh.
   He dreamed sweet dreams of butterflies
     and hoped that someday soon
   He'd be flying high up in the sky.

3. The little caterpillar woke and wriggled from his shell,
   Feeling something very new.
   And then he saw his pretty wings as they began to flutter,
   And up into the sky he flew.

   *(Chorus)*
   Butterfly, butterfly, now I fly so free,
   Butterfly, butterfly, can't believe it's me,
   Able to fly so high up in the sky,
   I'm a beautiful butterfly.

### THE BUMBLEBEE

The bumblebee keeps busy
Drinking nectar from the flowers,
It's yellow and black from front to back,
And hums for hours and hours.

*Susan Nipp*

(Rimsky-Korsakov: *Flight of the Bumblebee* — 1900)

## BUGS

*Susan Nipp*                                    *Traditional*

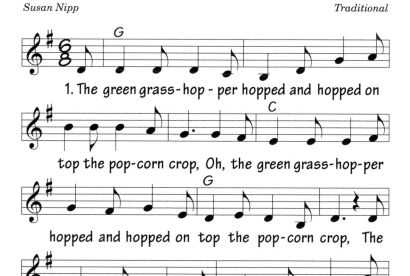

1. The green grass-hop-per hopped and hopped on

top the pop-corn crop, Oh, the green grass-hop-per

hopped and hopped on top the pop-corn crop, The

green grass - hop - per hopped and hopped on

18

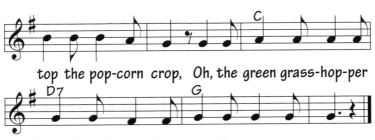

top the pop-corn crop, Oh, the green grass-hop-per

hopped and hopped on top the pop-corn crop.

2. The inchworm arched and inched his way along the brownish branch...

3. The dragonfly flew fast for fun while flitting on four wings...

4. The red ants hurried as they scurried all around the ground...

5. I sat on the ants and got ants in my pants and ran fast to get rid of the ants...

# ANIMAL ACTION

Move to the rhythm, move to the beat,
Move your body and move your feet.

Birds fly,
Rabbits hop,
Fish swim,
Frogs kerplop!

Ants march,
Worms wiggle,
Peacocks strut,
Jellyfish jiggle.

Move to the rhythm, move to the beat,
Move your body and move your feet.

Monkeys swing,
Lions stalk,
Eagles soar,
People walk.

Penguins waddle,
Kangaroos jump,
Mice scurry,
Camels galumph.

Move to the rhythm, move to the beat,
Move your body and move your feet.

*Pam Boall*

*It's a beautiful, sunny day. Let's get in the boat and row down the stream.*

## ROW, ROW, ROW YOUR BOAT

E. O. Lyte

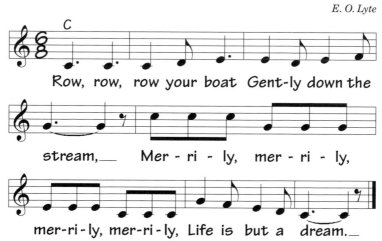

Row, row, row your boat Gent-ly down the stream,___ Mer - ri - ly, mer - ri - ly, mer-ri-ly, mer-ri-ly, Life is but a dream.___

*It's getting cold and windy! Row faster!*

Row, row, row your boat
Gently down the stream,
Merrily, merrily, merrily, merrily,
Life is but a dream.

22

There are rain clouds ahead! We need to find shelter. Row even faster!

**Row, row, row your boat**
**Gently down the stream,**
**Merrily, merrily, merrily, merrily,**
**Life is but a dream.**

It's raining! It's pouring!

Row to shore!

Jump out of the boat!

Tie up the boat!

Run for cover!

Whew!

## MOTORCYCLE

*Susan Nipp*                    *Susan Nipp*

Hop on, on my mo-tor-cy-cle, Fire up,

let's go, We're off on my mo-tor-cy-cle,

We're off, let's hit the road.___

Rid - in' on my mo - tor - cy - cle,

24

Ab

rid - in' on my mo - tor - cy - cle,

Fm          G7        Cm

Rid-in' on my mo-tor-cy-cle, rid-in' down the road.

Cm

Rid - in', rid - in',

Fm          G7        Cm

Rid-in' on my mo-tor-cy-cle, rid-in' down the road.

25

*All aboard! Let's go, Little Blue Engine.*

## LITTLE BLUE ENGINE

Susan Nipp                                                                Susan Nipp

1. "Lit - tle Blue En - gine, Lit - tle Blue En - gine,"

called the lit - tle toys, "O - ver the moun - tain,

there's a pa - rade for all the girls and boys.

Can you pull us o - ver the top and down the oth - er

side?" "I'll do my best," said the

Lit - tle Blue En - gine. "Hold on for the ride."

"I think I can, I think I can," the Lit - tle Blue En - gine

huffed, "I think I can, I think I can," the

Lit - tle Blue En - gine puffed, "I think I can, I

think I can," the Lit - tle Blue En - gine tugged. "I

think I can, I think I can," the

Lit - tle Blue En - gine chugged.

2. The toys began to hope and smile as the train moved down the track,
   "I'm not very big, but I can try," the engine smiled back.
   Faster, faster, the engine climbed up to the mountain top,
   The toys all cheered as the Little Blue Engine said, "I will not stop."

   *(Chorus)*

3. The Little Blue Engine pulled the train with all her strength and will,
   With one big puff she reached the top, then started down the hill,
   "Hurray, hurray, we knew you could," the little toy band cried,
   "We'll make it to the big parade 'cuz the Little Blue Engine tried."

   *(Chorus)*

"I thought I could, I thought I could,…"

## AIRPLANE

*Susan Nipp*

*Susan Nipp*

Sit-ting in the cock-pit of my air-plane, ___

Start-ing en-gine num-ber one, ___ Start-ing en-gine

num-ber two, ___ Rum - ble, _____

Mov-ing down the run-way, fast-er and fast-er,

Mov-ing down the run-way, fast-er and fast-er,

Lift off! Fly - ing, fly - ing up in the

28

sky, Fly - ing, fly - ing, I'm up so high,

Lift-ing up,      div-ing down,      Bank-ing left,

bank-ing right,      Fly-ing, fly-ing, high in the sky.

Run - way in    sight,    flaps    down,_____

Glid - ing, glid - ing, glid - ing    down.

Glid - ing, glid - ing, now it's touch - down.

## RACE CAR

Susan Nipp

*Traditional*

1. Driv-in' down the race-track just as fast as I can,
Fast as I can, fast as I can,
Driv-in' down the race-track just as fast as I can,
How I want to win this race.